BACK HOME Again

Aint no place
I'd rather be
Than back home again
In Tennessee

BACK HOME Again

Words and pictures by
Joe Clark, HBSS

**Privately printed
The Lynchburg
Hardware and
General Store
Lynchburg, Tenn.**

Photo by Junebug Clark 1981

Foreword

Four decades' worth of "down home" art produced by Joe Clark represents but a fraction of his prodigious photographic output (he has a half-million negatives on file—and he was well into his career before he began saving them.) This is Book Twelve on Tennessee alone. When he, his cameras and notebook revisit his beginnings, the result predictably is a loving characterization of a culture untouched by most of his audience.

Herein he has resurrected photographs from the Thirties, to establish nostalgic intent. As the pages move into the Forties and Fifties, he enforces the perception that while fashions and car design and music and other societal appendages undergo alteration, the hill-country mode remains stable, responding only vaguely to the surface trendiness which obsesses more crowded parts of North America.

The other facets of Joseph Benjamin Clark ("Joe for my grandpappy, Benjamin for Franklin") confirms that nobody is slipping anything by our man with the lenses. Chairmen and presidents of vast corporations address him respectfully by his first name. Street people, relaxed or on the prod, treat him as if they knew him from some other place. Many people are aware, in fact, that his film technique is by no means limited to set scenes; he has often responded instantly to the urgencies of national news stories. He has encapsulized, with one flick of the shutter, the savageries of riots, and fought off tears when a view of human conduct at its worst was presented to him.

In tranquil moments, he might choose to corn-pone you to pieces. One dares not routinely ask how the day goes. "Comin' round the mountain", that's how it goes anew and anew, his words, lingering over themselves.

He can date his family back to the Cumberland Gap of 1795, not as a vain claim to heritage—he couldn't find vanity on an otherwise bare plate—but simply to establish his credentials in that part of his realm. Happily

meandering past three score and ten, he decorates his trail with reflective commentary. "A rabbit runs faster than a dog because it thinks it has a better reason." And: "Who tells the animals about sex?" Or: "In school work, I was about what you'd call a backward child today. In them days, you were just stupid."

He dropped out of one-room Providence Elementary School in Powell Valley in the fifth grade. He did not renew his formal education until he was in his thirties. "I could hardly read or write. I took an English course from a correspondence school."

"After I learned to read a little, I read in Arthur Brisbane's column that the way to learn to think was by typing, so I bought a Royal portable typewriter. The way I really learned to write was by writin' to the editors of the Detroit News and the Detroit Free Press. I had six letters in the News one day, under different names."

Such gentle subterfuge is not his forte, compassion is. On the street for five days and nights during Detroit's 1967 riot, he never once filmed a looter's face. "I didn't want any identification," he said later. "I thought to myself then, 'These people are caught up in something.' I'd see a guy at a burning building takin' stuff. How do I know he maybe is not saving it for the owner? Now that's not likely, but why take a chance?"

One could debate that judgment but not the moral certitude. No more than one would argue the straightforwardness of an inscription he once scrawled in a book: "To a girl who never chews tobacco with her mouth full."

It is suggested that you do as the young lady did: Roam easily among the following portraits and philosophical findings, extracting whatever you please. That's a present to you from Joe.

JAMES C. JONES
Detroit Bureau Chief
Newsweek Magazine

Homefolk

There are folks that are, and folks that were
And folks that used to be
But there ain't no folks like the old home folks
Back home in Tennessee.

hbss

Introduction

This is a book of words and visuals of America past and present. Of an America that was and is. Of a land of hardships and pleasures. Of a land of freedom and achievement. Of work, humor and fun. Of tall stories and true stories. A land of dreams. Of dreams adreaming and of dreams fulfilled.

The old general store all boarded up by the roadside has long since been replaced by the supermarket. But the old general store once had its place. It not only offered the storebought luxuries of life but was also a kind of magical community center where folks stopped by to banter and exchange news and gossip.

Likewise the blacksmith shop where the rural American went to get his wagons, plows, grain cradles, and other tools, utensils and artifacts repaired and mended.

The water-powered gristmill. The old mill wheel first gave way to the one lunger, "stationary" gasoline engine. And then the big mills took over the grinding of grain into flour and meal. An important part of the American community ever since America was born, became things of the dim, misty past. There's hardly a farmer left who has seen the miller grind his grain into flour or meal.

And the springhouse was around long before the icebox and the refrigerator. Those were the days when we had fresh churned butter and real buttermilk with tiny chunks of butter swimming around in it. And when we cooled delicious watermelons in the cool stream from the spring. And fresh skimmed cream for our coffee. Not many folks today can even remember a hot cup of coffee with real fresh skimmed cream and a tiny chunk of fresh-churned butter floating on top. That was coffee for the Gods. Coffee nowadays has been mechanized to death.

And the one-room school where you knew intimately every kid in school. From the first through the eighth grade. It had its limitations but it wasn't all bad either. Still many of these one-room school buildings sit rotting by our rural roadsides so they are not so far in our dim distant past as we sometimes think.

And as long as a body had an axe there was no need to worry about fuel or energy shortages. You just chopped yourself a big pile of wood and dared winter to do its worst. And your only worries about mileage was how many miles you could get from a pair of storebought shoes. Those old days had their drawbacks but for those of us who lived them they also have a host of fine memories.

Cars are a wonderful thing. Everybody gets a heap of pleasure and satisfaction out of them. And when the gas runs out we are gonna find it mighty hard to get along without them. But not many folks today know the pleasure of walking two or three miles to school. Or to the grocery store, or to the gristmill, or the blacksmith shop. Or even a hundred yards or so to the springhouse. Those are forgotten hardships and forgotten pleasures.

And following a mule down miles and miles of corn rows in the hot sun. And then currying and caring for and feeding the mule after the days work was done not to mention feeding the cows and chickens and pigs and things. That's all been replaced with air-conditioned tractors with high-fi radios and foamy cushioned seats for our tender loving butts to sit on while we work.

These, too, are grand and glorious days. We just might be smart if we spent more time enjoying 'em and less time making mountains out of our little problems.

Certainly we couldn't possibly live today without disco, television and movies. They are all educational, entertaining and wonderful. But there is still something to be said for old fashioned apple-peelings, corn-huskins, and lasses making partys. They all entailed a heap of hard work. But the work seemed to make the fun and the girls seem sweeter. And I still feel that Aunt Liz Powell had a grip on the tail of a small truth when she said "Folks nowadays have done set around and watched movies and television and things til their brains has dried up and blowed away."

Otherwise, how can we find time to complain when there's so much to be thankful for. _Joe Clark,_ hbss

Roads

Roads

Roads lead ever out and on
  To places far away,
Some to places new and fresh
 And some to yesterday.
        hbss

Way Down Yonder in Tennessee

Where the wild birds sing from the old oak tree
 And the whippoorwills call from the top of the hill
And the hound dogs bay in the valley so free
 And the mountaineer fires his moonshine still.

Where the fair maids smile to the barefoot boys
 And the sun sinks softly in the golden west
And the breezes whisper of a million joys
 Down in the land where I love the best.
        hbss

The Hurrying Kind

Who wants to travel so fast and straight
On a freeway that streaks across the state
Or on a jet plane that flys so high
Through the misty clouds up in the sky?
Not I! Not I! Says I! Says I!
Let the demons race and the buzzards fly.
Hell is filled with the hurrying kind
Give me a footpath and peace of mind.
The devil meant for the rats to race
I'll take time to enjoy the place.

hbss

Grandpa

One cherished moment
Long gone by
Returns again
To cause a sigh.

hbss

There is nothing that ever pleasured me
Like visiting with Grandpa in Tennessee.
                                        hbss

Energy

We didn't use no energy
back in the olden days.

We just chopped ourselves
a big pile of wood
and then dared winter to do its worst.

Chopping wood was women's work
But it took a man to cut corn.

Mules

Mule Musings

I pull this plow the live long day,
For this I get but little pay,
And when that weary sun goes down
I'm much too tired to horse around.

Yet life is not all that it seems,
Both man and mule have their dreams;
Of pastures green and clover high,
Of golden mansions in the sky.

The man I own who follows me
Is kind and good as he can be;
He guides the plow the whole day through;
I know that he is weary, too.

It behooves me not to complain
If man is born with little brain;
When he follows me the livelong day
And sees I get my oats and hay.

Moral:

And now my friends, as you can see,
A mule's no better off than we.

hbss

You Aint Never Lived

You aint never lived
   And don't know how
Til you've followed a mule
   Behind a plow.

Til you've followed a mule
   And plowed the ground
You aint never traveled
   Nor been around.

You just don't know nothin
   About humankind
Til you've spent a year lookin
   At a mule's behind.

hbss

Some people work like mules
and some mules loaf like people.

hbss

Aint no place
I'd rather be
Than back home
In Tennessee.

hbss

Mileage

Mileage was not reckoned so much
in miles per gallon as how much mileage
one could get from a pair of shoes.

hbss

Growing Old

Someday we'll all grow old
    And start busting at the seams
Then we can sit on the porch
    And talk about our dreams.

hbss

Blacksmith Shop

The Blacksmith Shop

The blacksmith shop was where everybody went
When the wagon got broke or the plow got bent.

The smith could fix anything you ever did see
Whether a broken churn or a cracked whippletree.

I can see him now as he stood by the door
Content on his face, his feet on the floor.

There I found much pleasure when I was a boy
The talk and the work was a thing of pure joy.

hbss

Apple Butter

Making Apple Butter

Peeling rosy-red apples for winter's vittles
And making apple butter in the copper
kettle.

hbss

Springhouse

The Old Springhouse

The old springhouse was such a wonderful place
With the milk and butter all over the place
And sometimes a melon to cool in the stream
And the top of the milk for the coffee cream.   hbss

Butter and
Egg Money

Butter and eggs used to didn't cost anything.
They were homegrown.

In fact, the surplus was called "Butter and egg money."
And you used it to buy luxuries like sugar, coffee,
baking-powder and coal oil. And even storebought clothes.

hbss

The Old General Store

There was a place that aint no more
Since they boarded up the general store
A place of memories it stands today
By the rural roadside rotting away.

hbss

School

One-room School

Deserted now is that
   One-room school
Where a barefoot lad
   Learned the golden rule.

Many a kid learned more on the
long walk to school than he learned
all day long sitting on them soft
easy benches.

        hbss

Childhood Days

Those Golden Days

Oh, those days, those golden days
　Those days of sweetest joy
Swinging on the old barn gate
　Back when I was a boy.

　　　　　　　　　hbss

My Castle

I'll build my castle of glowing dreams
　Upon a mountain high
Where I can see the deep green valley
And touch the azure sky.

　　　　　　　　　hbss

Tillers Of The Soil

To plow and plant and wield a hoe
Them were the days that ain't no mo.

to rest a mite and take it slow
In those old days of long ago.

hbss

Harvesting

Harvesting Grain

    It's not too long since grain
had to be harvested by hand.
    Every stalk had to be cut by hand
then gathered into bundles, tied by hand,
shocked then hauled into one location
and fed into a threshing machine by hand.

Then came the combine which was
pulled by horses. With this machine
a man could ride in comfort and cut,
bundle and tie as much wheat, rye or
oats as four or five men could cut, bundle and
tie by hand.

About the same time came great engines
with as much power as several horses.
And the machine age had arrived.

hbss

Machines

Old Machinery

Old machinery sits idle
  In the noonday sun
For father time moves on
  Their day's work is done.

                    hbss

Gristmill

The Old Millwheel

By a clear, sparkling stream
  Sat the old mill wheel
And the farmer brought his corn
  To be ground into meal.

hbss

"All the good things aint been done yet
And all the bad things aint happened yet."

hbss

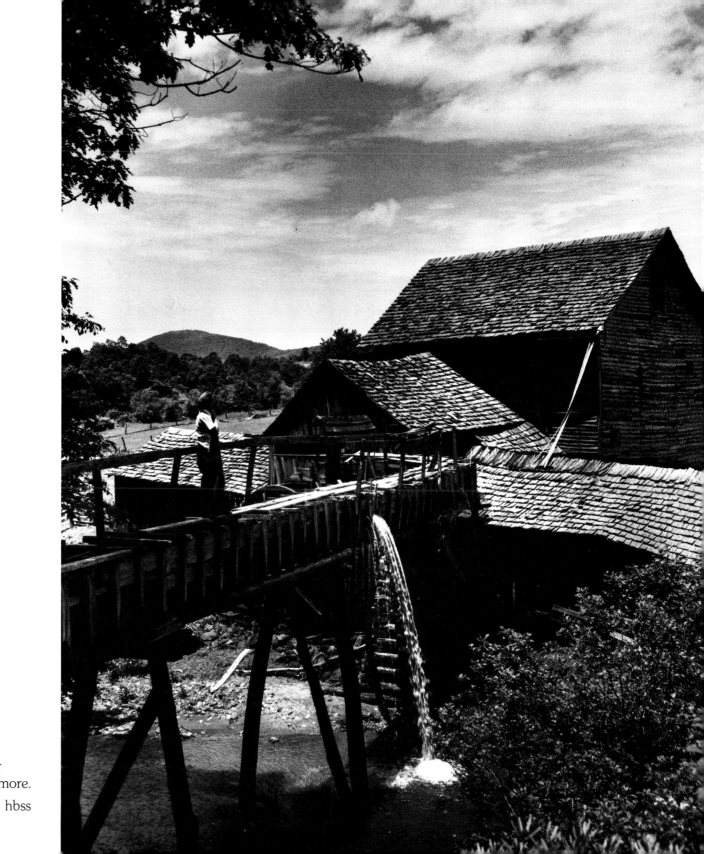

The Old Gristmill

The miller sits in the millhouse door
But the old gristmill don't grind no more.

hbss

Outhouses

The Outhouse

Whether it was of brick or stone
Or built firm and strong of wood alone
There was a place we used to know
Where we went when we had to go.

hbss

But the prettiest sight I ever did see
Was under the flowering dogwood tree.

Moonshine

Corn is what grows on a hillside
in Tennessee
And you buy it by the jug.

Corn is what grows in The Tennessee Hills.
And you drink it from a jug.

Pappy's Still

When my troubles I would shed,
A bleeding heart or aching head,
I take the road to yonder hill
And sip the booze from Pappy's still.

hbss

J. D.

Up a little hollow
    In the hills of Tennessee
They make the finest whiskey
    That ever there could be.

hbss

My Darlin in Tennessee

My Darlin in Tennessee

Where the roads are kinder windey
   And the hills are tall and steep
And the beauty of the scenery
   Is enough to make you weep.

There I left my little darlin
   In her cabin on the hill;
I wanna go back to see her
   But I know I never will.

For my heart was born to
wander
   And my soul is wild and free
And a sittin by the fireside
   Was never meant for me.

And the yonder keeps a callin
   And my feet are never still
And I'll never see my darlin
   In her cabin on the hill.

                              hbss

Memories

What keeps me
  So young and spry
Is memories
  Of days gone by.

                    hbss

By The Fireplace

By the fireplace so long ago
With shadows dancing to and fro
When I was young and times were old
There, many wondrous tales were told.

Tales of daring deeds well done
Of villains conquered by the gun,
Of storms that beat the briny sea
Of many things that used to be.

Of deserts hot and bare and wide
Of men who won and men who tried,
Of lands so rich and far away
Of feet that found a better way.

Of treasure chests so often found
Of fertile plains and hallowed ground
Of trees that covered all the land
Of men so brave who made their stand.

Of savage men who roamed so free
Of scalpings and of massacree,
Of ghastly things that were a fright
Of ghosts that traveled in the night.

Of battles won and battles lost
Of streams so wide that were crossed,
Of lands beyond the setting sun
Of maidens wooed and maidens won.

By the fireside so long ago
With shadows dancing to and fro,
When I was young and times were old
So many wondrous tales were told.

hbss

A Winding Path

Have You Ever Walked a Winding Path?

A path that climbed across a hill;
A path that passed beside a well?

A path that crept across a ridge
A path that ran across a bridge?

A path that loafed along the way,
A path that wound along the bay?

A path that knew no stranger's feet,
A path that led to someone sweet?

A path that wandered through the snow,
A path where flowered meadows grow?

A path that went to one-room school,
A path beside a limpid pool?

A path beneath the apple trees,
A path to childhood memories?

hbss

Down a lonely road
   I walked one day
And all my cares
   Were far away.

hbss

Animals

Animals

Animals are like people, so they say,
Each has its own little whimsical way.
Animals don't cuss nor fight and steal
But a goose and a horse will make a deal
And a cat and a goose, just think of that
Put them together and they'll have a spat.

hbss

Meetin'

The Sabbath Day

Sunday being the Sabbath Day
We went to church to love and pray.

hbss

The log church shown in these pictures
was built in the winter of 1795-6
while George Washington was still president.

Funeral

Eternity

A little boy sat by the riverside
Fishing and dreaming and watching the tide;
Watching the tide as the river rolled on,
Before he knew it his youth was gone.

An old man sat by the riverside
Fishing and dreaming and watching the tide
Watching the tide as the river rolled on
Dreaming of his youth a long time gone.

No longer they sit by the riverside
Fishing and dreaming and watching the tide;
Both to the grave have already gone
But the river and the tide still roll on.

hbss

Finis

No one ever comes here to stay
Each and everyone has his day
Then great or small we pass away.

hbss

Making Molasses

Molasses were made from the juice of sorgum cane a cane that is somewhat similar to sugar cane. A field of sorgum cane looks somewhat similar to a field of Indian corn except that there are no ears on sorgum cane. The seeds are on top of the stalks similar to broom corn seeds.

First the long slender leaves or blades were stripped from the cane stalks by hand and while the stalks were still standing in the field.

Then the stalks were cut, the seed heads were cut off, and the stalks hauled in wagons to the cane mill where the juice was squeezed out of the stalks by feeding them between steel rollers that were generally turned by mule power.

Once the juice was squeezed out it was poured into long vats and boiled down into a syrup called Sorgum Molasses. It took about ten gallons of cane juice to make a gallon of molasses.

Sorgum molasses has a strong tangy taste and was often used in cooking as a sweetener. It was at its best in molasses cookies. It was also a pretty fair syrup if you mixed in lots of fresh butter to soften the tangy taste. It also helped some if you were real hungry.

The two outstanding features of molasses making were (1) the prodigious amount of work that went into making a gallon of molasses and (2) the wonderful amount of partying and courtin that went on at a molasses makin. It was generally called a STIR-OFF.

Joe Clark, HBSS

Harvesting sorgum cane. The cane stalks in this picture have already been hand-stripped of their long narrow blades, or fodder, and the stalks are being cut and headed and made ready for hauling to the mill.

We ground all night
　And we ground all day
But a boys work
　Never went away.

The crazy old mule
　Went round and round
But it seems the cane
　Could never get ground.

And those, My Friend,
　Were the days of old
The glorious days
　So I've been told.

　　　　　hbss

But it wasn't really all work
and no play at stir-off time.
As the 'lasses began to boil
down the blood of the young
folks also began to boil.
Music began to appear out of the
nowhere. And out of the nowhere
came young folks. Lots of young
folks to dance and frolic in the
moonlight.

And the lasses boiled
    And the music played
And the lads and lassies
    Danced and swayed.

And as the night wore on
    The lads grew bolder
And a lad caught his lassie
    And kissed and holdher.

As the lasses boiled down
   The folks gathered nigher
To watch the lasses boil
   And warm by the fire.

Then they sampled the lasses,
    They tasted so sweet
Then they strained them into cans
    And took 'em home to eat.
                                    hbss

First Date

When I was a teenager in the hills of Tennessee fall was always the most wonderful time of year. We kept the hills jumping with such things as bean shellings, corn huskins, and spelling bees. But the grandest and most wonderful of all these parties was Stir-Off Time. Here the older folks would squeeze the juice from the canestalks and boil it down into molasses. And the young folks would gather in from miles and miles around to square dance in the cane stalks, play singing games and make whoopee.

And, along about midnight we would all gather around the boiling molasses and the warming fire to listen to the old timers tell ghost stories until everyone was most afraid to go home.

This year things were different. A new girl had come to the Tennessee hills. The Beasons had moved into the valley from somewhere over in Kentucky. And their daughter, Linda, was as purty as a possum up a simmon tree.

All the fellers kept a paying Linda a lot more tention than I thought they oughter. But Linda kept purty close to me so I finally got up nerve enough to ast her could I walk her home.

It was my first date. And walking with Linda behind her Pa and Ma was dist about as near to walking them

You could hug the girls
  And tell 'em lies
But you couldn't resist
  them devilish eyes.

            hbss

golden streets as I ever hoped to get. But there was dist one little teeny fly in the buttermilk.

Linda lived four miles up the valley, acrost Bald Ridge in Slocum Hollow. And I lived three miles down the valley, past Red Hill and acrost Towne Creek. And the closer I got to Linda's house the more uneasy I got about that seven-mile trip back home. It meant that I'd have to walk right past Old Settlers Graveyard. After midnight! Alone! All my life I'd listened to old timers tell hairy ghost stories about Old Settlers Graveyard.

Then there was Goblers Knob where the Indians, it was said, once lured an old settler to his doom by gobbling like a turkey. Then they cut him to pieces and scattered the pieces over the landscape. Anybody unlucky enough to be traveling alone in the neighborhood of Goblers Knob on a dark night was apt to encounter some of these gory pieces of the old settler floating about in wisps of translucent mist looking for each other. Then there were all the fellows who had been paying so much mind to Linda at the Stir-Off. They were almost certain to be lurking in the woods along the way and up to no good in so far as I was concerned.

So when Linda's Pa suggested that I stay the night in their spare room I gave him no chance to change his mind.

It was a new log room they had built onto the house during the summer but hadn't yet gotten around to chinking the cracks. This being the first frosty night of fall the cold wind kept a pouring in through an extra big crack that happened to be right along side of my bed and freezing my back. So I got up and I gathered up all my clothes and I wadded 'em up and I chinked that pesky crack with'm. Then I curled up and went to sleep.

Along towards morning I woke with that cold icy wind a pouring in on my back again. A quick check showed me that my chinkin was all gone. So I peeked out through the crack and there, outlined against the new white frost, was an old cow. Happily chewing on the last bite of my clothes.

Here I was a big dumb country boy. On his first date. Seven miles from home. And not a stitch of clothes to my name. Just in case this has never happened to you I'd like to tell you that I was in quite a picklement.

Lucky for me I didn't have to waste no time making decisions. What to do was already spelled out loud and clear. I could see by the stars that there was jist about an hour of darkness left. So, traveling light and totally streamlined, I split the frosty wind down Slocum Hollow like an arrow, angled up Bald Ridge and shot past Old Settlers Graveyard so fast that no ghost would have had a ghost of a chance at catching me. On down Bald Ridge and on down the valley. Slowing not a whit for sawbriar patches nor sassafrass thickets.

I flew past Goblers Knob so fast that it would have took two Indians just to see me: One to say, 'Yonder he comes!'' and one to say, ''Yonder he goes!''

I had begun to puff a little so I tackled the steep side of Red Hill. But I picked up enough speed on the down side to cross Towne Creek with a mighty splash.

I looked up and there atop the hill, sitting black against a faintly reddening sky, was Home!

As I passed through the barn lot the old rooster gave out with the first crow of morning. I had made it. While it was still dark. But with enough bruises and briar scratches to last a lifetime.

As I passed the kitchen I heard Pa starting a fire in the kitchen stove. Lucky for me my brother had left the bedroom window open. I slid acrost the window sill and started grabbing for some clothes. I had barely got dressed when Ma called me to grind the coffee.

At the breakfast table Ma said, "Son, you look a little peaked this morning. I must make you some sassafrass tea."

Joe Clark, hbss

Lynchburg

If Lynchburg keeps on growing
it may one day get to be a small town.

            hbss

Lynchburg

Nobody hardly ever
gets lost in Lynchburg.

            hbss

Life was meant
for people to enjoy.

hbss

Things are different I am told
Some are new and some are old.
I cannot tell (there is no test)
Which is worse or which is best.

hbss

There is a youth
  That never dies
While mischief hides
  Behind the eyes.

hbss

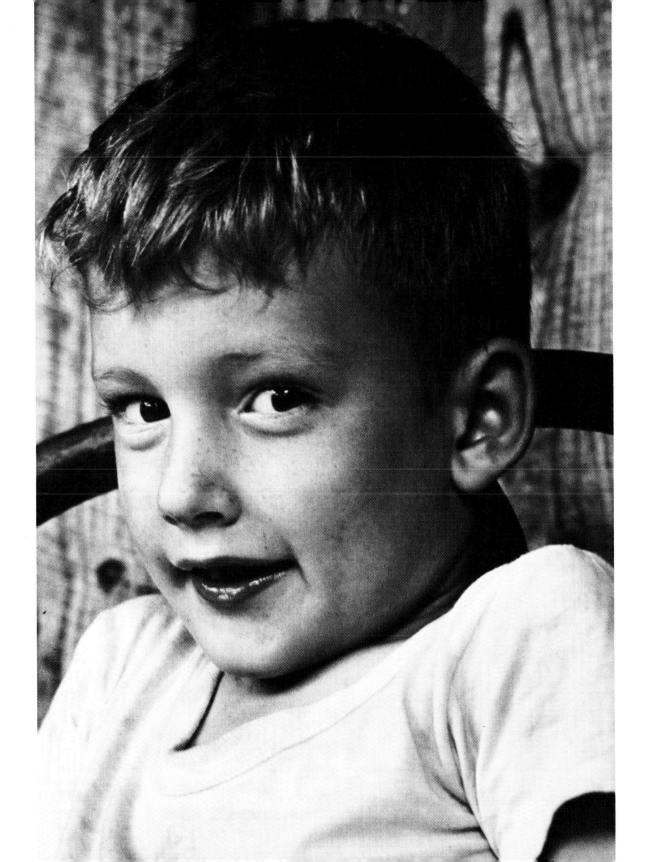

Margret Tolly

Deep in the heart
 Is where beauty lies
And lights the world
 Throgh the eyes.

hbss

Lynn Tolly

Like wood some people grow
more beautiful with age.

Louise Daniel
   has successfully run a large
farm since her husband died in
1936.

Miss Mary Bobo
   Has run Lynchburg's most
elite boarding house for more
than seventy years.

THE ALBINO WHOOTER

Some Tall Tales and Other True Stories from Tennessee

GREAT GRANDPAPPY

Over the years Tennessee has produced some of the greatest people of all time; but the greatest of them all as everybody already knows was my Great Grandpappy, Joe Clark.

But I'd like to tell you about the time that Great Grandpappy saved the settlement from starvation. And I don't mean that he did it by hopping into his red roadster and cadillacing down to the super market for a few cans of beans. Nosirreee! Back in them days a man had to look death square in the teeth to bring home the bear meat.

And the women didn't go in for none of this soft storebought cooking either. They loved to skin out their own bear meat and hand-broil them big juicy steaks over an open fire.

Grandpappy was just a young man back in them days and some of the settlers claimed that he was just a mite lazy. But he wasn't lazy atall. Great Grandpappy just didn't believe in charging around fraying his nerves and wasting his energy. He knew how to relax. Besides he wore a pair of them old fashioned pants, with the silver buckles at the knees, that were three sizes too big for him. They not only let him in for a lot of kidding but they made him seem to move even less than he did. It took a great deal of movement just to take up the slack. But, as you'll see later, they were to play an important role in saving the colony.

Well, it was the year of the hard winter. The food was all gone and game was scarce. Even Davey Crocket hadn't so much as shot a flying squirrel all winter. So they called a meeting to decide what to do. And it was decided that the men would all go hunting.

At daybreak the next morning the men all set out in different directions to scour the woods for some meat to eat. But as the great round sun was setting in the golden west they all came a tromping back into the settlement with nothing more than a lot of sore feet. So they called a meeting for the purpose of giving up.

Nobody had noticed that Great Grandpappy hadn't showed up yet.

You see, he had only gone over the hill out of sight of the settlement and then sat down on the sunnyside of a tree to do some thinking. He was a great one to think things out. And he must have fallen asleep because, just as the settlers were about to vote to give up, he had a nightmare and dreamed that he was way out in the woods all by himself and lost. Being a man of action he grabbed his trusty rifle and fired straight up into the air to signal for help.

Now it happened that there was five big old fat turkeys a settin on a limb directly above Great Grandpappy's head and his rifle ball went smack through the middle of that limb and split it wide open and them turkeys' toes slipped right down into the crack. And then, like a steel trap, the crack closed up on them turkeys' toes and held them fast. And then that bullet went straight on up and came straight back down, and there was this big old fat bear that had heard Great Grandpappy snoring and snook up to see if it wasn't another bear, and thet bullet came down and hit him on the head and killed him dead.

Great Grandpappy always did things in a big way and he had loaded so much powder into his gun that it kicked him head over heels into the river. This woke him up and he came out of that river a coughing and a spluttering. But it was a good thing that he was young and strong because them oversized pants of his had schooped up so many big fat fish that it took a strong young man just to carry them. In fact they were so heavy that one of Great Grandpappy's gallus buttons popped off and killed a big old fat rabbit.

Just as the settlers were about to vote to give up Great Grandpappy came a strolling out of the woods a carrying that big old fat rabbit in one hand and a dragging that big old fat bear with the other. And all of them big old fat fish were still a flopping around in his big oversized pants. And over his shoulder he carried that limb with them five big old fat turkeys a hanging from it.

While all the womenfolk set to work a cleaning and a cooking all that fine fresh meat the menfolk sent out for a couple of cases of beer and they all had a real old time feast.

And that, Dear Friends, is the honest true story of how Great Grandpappy saved the settlement.

And it's a good thing, too, because without the settlement there would be no Tennessee and without Tennessee there would be no United States. And without a United States there would be nobody for the rest of the world to blame its troubles on.

hbss

THE CITY PREACHER

The meetin' house was full to the rafters this Sunday morning, not so much because we had a new school educated preacher from the city as because of his text. The word was out that he was going to preach on Ghosts.

Everybody leaned forward just a bit as he announced that he had come to the Cumberlands because he had heard that folks around here still believed in ghosts. Then everybody just about fell off the benches when he added, "Before I'm through this morning I will have proven to you conclusively that there is no such thing as a ghost. Educated, civilized people do not believe in them."

Well, as it turned out, that feller was a pretty smooth talker. And, before he was through I could tell that there were some people who were beginning to believe, at least a little bit. In fact, I think that me and my brother was among the believers.

Anyway, after dinner we went out to the barn and got to talking about it and my brother said, "You know if that's true about there being no ghosts there'd be some mighty good possum hunting on Goblers Knob."

Well, the possums had been pretty well caught out this season already. But nobody had ever hunted possums on Goblers Knob on account of it was haunted by the ghost of an old settler that the Indians had killed there many, many years ago. And besides there was a mound on top of Goblers Knob that everybody said was an Indian graveyard. Still, if there wasn't no ghosts somebody was missing some awful good possum hunting.

Between the two of us we sort of talked each other into playing hookey from meetin' Sunday night and going possum hunting on Goblers Knob. And we was doing mighty fine, too. Cause in hardly no time atall we had us two big old fat live possums apiece.

And then that fool dog of ours come a chasing a big

old black bear right down the path behind us. When we made a dash to get out of the way we tripped over a log in the darkness and all four of our possums got clean away.

That was quite a blow, all that nice fat possum meat getting away like that. But the night was young yet so we kept moving up the Knob and pretty soon our dog treed a coon up a big old chestnut tree.

We knowed that even if there wern't no ghosts it was still a sin to chop down a tree on Sunday. But then we looked at that big old fat coon setting up there and reasoned that maybe it really wasn't a sin if you chopped it down after dark on Sunday night.

That tree was so confounded big that it took us quite a spell but we finally laid it down kerboom right down the hillside. And then we ran down to get our coon. But he got away on account of the tree fell on our dog and killed him. And him the best dadburned possum and coon dog in the valley.

When you're licked you might just as well admit it and give up. And we certainly wasn't doing so good up to now so we cut across the top of the Knob for home.

Right smack on top of the Knob we come to this big old Indian Chief. And he said, "I Chief Hapwuwango. You boys very kind. You let Indian's friends, the possums and the coons, live. I reward you." Well, we hadn't exactly looked at it that way but Pappy had always said never to look a gift horse in the mouth so we kept quiet.

And Chief Hapwuwango sat right down and wrote us out a check for a hundred dollars. This seemed a little strange at the time because everybody knew that Chief Hapwuwango and all his braves had been dead for more than a hundred years already. But we remembered again about the gift horse.

We felt just like a couple of rich capitalists the next day when my brother shoved that check through the window to the banker. But the banker just took one look at it and shoved it right back. This made my brother pretty mad and he said something to the banker about disrespecting Chief Hapwuwango's signature and him been dead over a hundred years. But the banker said that he had no intention of disrespecting Chief Hapwuwango's signature. He couldn't cash the check because it was made out on Sunday and it was against the law for the bank to cash a check that was dated on Sunday.

Well, the next Sunday me and my brother was back in church again. And we listened careful to everything that city preacher said. And when he passed around the collection plate we put that whole hundred-dollar check in it.

hbss

GRANDPAPPY AND THE LITTLE DETAILS

It's funny what a little cold snap will do to people.

A bunch of the fellows was a sittin around Ken Silers Punkin Patch soaking up a little heat. (Ken's Punkin Patch is as near to the old general store as any place you'll find anywhere these days.)

Anyway, while we was a soakin up some of Ken's heat the fellows got to spinnin yarns of one kind or another.

And, you know me, I've allus been too modest ever to mention any of the many daring deeds or heroic achievements of my ancestors.

But I couldn't help thinkin of my Grandpappy. He was allus a great one for little details. In fact, lookin back on it, I guess that was the real secret of Grandpappy's Greatness. Tending to little details.

When he needed meat Grandpappy never grabbed his rifle and went a chargin off into the woods like his neighbors did. No sirreee!

In fact, Grandpappy often said, "Show me a man a luggin a bear out of the woods and I'll show you a feller who is not a thinkin man."

When the bear meat run low at Grandpappy's house he'd take out his barlowe and cut hisself a small willow branch. And he'd strip all the leaves off that willow branch except the last three right on the very tip.

Then he'd calmly stroll into the woods until he came to a big old fat bear that was jist exactly to his likin.

Then Grandpappy would start ticklin that big old fat bear under the chin with the tip of that willow branch. And he'd keep at it until that big old fat bear would get so mad that he would come a chargin after Grandpappy.

Then Grandpappy would light out for home with that big old fat bear right on his tail and a grabbin at him at every jump.

As Grandpappy would top the last hill comin in sight of the cabin, with that big old fat bear a grabbin at the seat of his pants at every jump, he would give out with a big loud holler, and when Granny would hear Grandpappy's big loud holler she would open the front door. And the back door. Then she would stand by just as calm as you please.

When Grandpappy would come a chargin through the house with that big old fat bear right on his heels Granny would wait til he went out the back door. Then, real quick like, she would slam the back door right in that old bear's face.

This always confused the bear. It never failed. For a minit he couldn't figger where Grandpappy had went all of a sudden. And while he was a tryin to figger out what had happened Granny would tiptoe over and close the front door.

Then she had her bear meat right there in the house without nobody totin nothin nowhere.

All Granny had to do was grab that big old fat bear by the tail, bash his brains out against the mantlepiece, peel him out, spread the skin on the floor, toss the meat into the pot and, presto, she had herself a new living room rug and dinner on a cookin.

Granny allus used to say, "If the Good Lord hadn't aimed for you to use your brain he wouldn't of give it to you in the first place."

hbss

HAFFY

I've heard some mighty tall tales in my time. And I've spun a few yarns myself but no mortal man could ever dream up a story to equal the honest true facts about the obstreperous, grass-green wyooter with the long brown tail that once lived in the forest of Ingerside near the village of Kazzlekoo only a short trip by canoe and dog sled beyond the serene and sunny state of Tranquility deep in the hills of Tennessee.

This all happened back in the early days, some four million years ago when people were still shaped like round fuzzy balls with short stubby arms that seemed to disappear when folded against their fat round sides; and long, long skinny legs on which they didn't walk but hopped about pretty much like kangeroos.

The village of Kazzlekoo where these early type human beings lived and prospered for some twenty-thousand years was a quiet and peaceful village on the edge of Ingerside forest. And her brave warriors and bold hunters hunted the izzlepuss and ozzlefaz and the ferocious Snazzlefritz. And they also gathered the eggs of the famous flying snazzlepoo in Ingerside forest.

Indeed the Ingerside forest provided such a bountiful hunting ground that it is little wonder that the folks of Kazzlekoo grew fat and round like fuzzy round balls.

But this good life and bountiful living ground to a halt when the obstreperous, grass-green wyooter with the long brown tail moved into the forest and began to systematically devour the good citizens of Kazzlekoo. In fact, he had a habit of lingering in the protection of the tall izzle trees near the edge of Ingerside Forest and when a fat round citizen ventured too close a huge green paw would suddenly reach out, snatch up the hapless citizen, flip him high into the air much as a school boy would flip up a peanut. And, then as the hapless citizen came tumbling down, the obstreperous grass-green wyooter with the long brown tail would catch him in his huge open mouth and promptly swallow him whole at one gulp.

And, since the good citizens of Kazzlekoo had to venture into the forest for food the obstreperous, grass-green wyooter with the long brown tail became so expert at his little game that soon there were no citizens left in the whole of the village of Kazzlekoo.

I really mean that there was only one citizen left in the whole of the village of Kazzlekoo, and that was Haffy. Haffy wasn't really his real name. Everybody just called him Haffy because he was the village half-wit.

And the only reason that Haffy survived to be the only citizen of Kazzlekoo was on account of because of his not being very bright he was never allowed to go into the forest with the brave warriors and bold hunters of the village and so he never got near Ingerside Forest and the clutches of the obstreperous, grass-green wyooter with the long brown tail.

Finding himself all alone in the village Haffy grew lonely for, being the village half-wit, it had been his duty to keep the villagers happy and contented by making wisecracks and telling them bum jokes. And now Haffy missed their laughter and their good-natured jibing at him for being so dumb. And then he remembered how his pappy always used to have a habit of saying, "Haffy, my boy," he would say, Haffy, my boy, you are only a half-wit but if you can learn to think even a little bit you will be twice as smart as the bright boys who think that because they are bright they've got it made and don't have to think.

Now thinking, even just a little bit, is not easy for a half-wit so Haffy started thinking very hard and very small. Very small because he knew that he only needed to think just a little bit and very hard because it is very hard for a half-wit to think even just a little bit.

After thinking very hard and very small for a very long time Haffy finally hit upon a plan. To be sure it was a very small plan. But it was a plan.

First, to carry out his plan, he searched about until he found a very long and very strong canoe paddle. Then, grasping this paddle in both hands and carrying it much as a tight rope artist carries a balancing rod Haffy began his carefully careless sort of errotic approach to Ingerside Forest. He tried to make it seem that he did not realize that he was approaching Ingerside Forest because he didn't want the obstreperous grass-green wyooter with the long brown tail to know that he had a plan.

But he needn't have bothered because the obstreperous, grass-green wyooter with the long brown tail, knowing that Haffy was the village half-wit never even dreamed that Haffy had a plan. He just sat there happily hidden in the shade of the tall izzle trees and smiling smugly at the thought that he would soon devour the very last of the inhabitants of the village of Kazzlekoo.

And sure enough as Haffy set foot in the first shade of the tall brown izzle trees that giant green paw darted out and snatched up Haffy and flipped him high into the air.

Haffy, not being a bold hunter nor a brave warrior was scared out of his half-wits when he looked down from that tremendous height into the dark brown throat and the huge gaping mouth that waited to catch him on his downward flight.

But Haffy didn't have time to worry about that. He had to use all the half-wit he had just to carry out his plan. So he gripped his long, strong canoe paddle even tighter and held it above his head as if he were hanging from a trapeeze bar.

And then kerplunk that canoe paddle wedged itself between that obstreperous, grass-green wyooter's great brown jaws and propped his mouth wide open much as a porch post holds up a porch roof.

So startled was the obstreperous, grass-green wyooter with the long brown tail by this turn of events that he remained stunned for a minute or two.

And all the villagers seeing their chance while the obstreperous, grass-green wyooter's mouth was wedged wide open dashed out of the obstreperous, grass-green wyooter's stomach through his open mouth and hurried back to their village.

And there they voted Haffy the wisest of all their wise men. And made him Lord Mayor and High Potentate of the village where he reigned in peace and prosperity for fourteen-thousand years.

Because people in them days breathed unpolluted air and ate foods without artificial coloring they lived longer than they do nowadays.

And the obstreperous, grass-green wyooter with the long brown tail was so mortified at being outwitted by the village half-wit that he slunk away into the very middle of Ingerside forest and there hid himself in a dark dank cave, and so far as I know, there he still stays til this very day hiding and sulking in his dark dank cave.

Since this is all true facts there is no moral to this story; but if you will think even a little bit you might be able to come up with some kind of a moral.

Thank you for listening.

hbss

GRANDPAPPY WAS A THINKIN MAN

Some people are workers and some are thinkers. Folks often accused Grandpappy of being lazy. But Grandpappy thought a lot. In fact, many of the things that people wear and use today are things that Grandpappy thought about.

They didn't have these nice clean, fancy sidewalks for people to walk on back in them days and Granny was always jawing at Grandpappy for getting his socks so dirty. So Grandpappy up and thought about shoes to keep his socks clean. And now everybody's a wearin 'em.

Grandpappy loved bear meat and gravy. He could eat bear meat and gravy three times a day. Bear meat and gravy for breakfast. Bear meat and gravy for dinner. Bear meat and gravy for supper. Then, like as not, he'd raide the springhouse for bear meat and gravy at bedtime.

And that's how come that Grandpappy thought about the necktie that all men wear today to keep the gravy off their shirts.

And they didn't have these nifty smooth roads back in them days. Even at best it was bad enough riding around without any pavement, much less on square tires. So Grandpappy thought about the round tire that is just now being advertised.

When Grandpappy rode the pony express he noticed that the ponys got tired. In fact, they got so tired that he had to change to a fresh pony every ten miles. So Grandpappy thought about air mail. To give the ponys a rest. And, not only that, he also thought about putting glue on the backs of postage stamps. To keep the letters from falling off.

With all that thinkin' Grandpappy didn't have much time left for workin. And pretty soon the bills began to pile up. And the bill collectors got to hounding Grandpappy. And, sometimes, Grandpappy even thought about paying them.

—hbss

NEIGHBORS

In Old Settlers Graveyard on top of Bald Ridge in the Tennessee hills is the strangest grave I ever did see.

The marker at the head of this strange grave is not a tombstone but an almost brand new Oliver Hillside Plow. And the marker at the foot of this strange grave is an identical almost brand new Oliver Hillside Plow.

Instead of being covered with flowers, the grave is planted to corn.

It is the story of this strange grave that I'm about to tell.

Deadwood Underwood and Oliver Tolliver had been friends and adjoining neighbors for nigh onto forty years. They each owned a farm in Horseshoe Bend on Ripple Creek.

Deadwood Underwood's farm extends from the middle of Ripple Creek to the top of the West side of Razorback Ridge. And Oliver Tolliver's farm extends from the center of Ripple Creek to the top of the East side of Razorback Ridge, and thereby joining Deadwood Underwood's farm.

Such good friends have these two gentlemen been over the years that it has never been an unusual sight to see their two respective cows with tails tied together and hanging over Razorback Ridge while each grazed in her respective pasture.

One day, Oliver Tolliver and Deadwood Underwood stopped by Dal Gulley's General Store to jaw awhile. And while they were there, a drummer man by the name of Silvertongue Smith from the Oliver Plow Company did such a good job of peddling his Oliver Hillside Plow that Tolliver and Underwood each bought one and took it home with him in his wagon.

When spring rolled around, Oliver Tolliver planted the East side of Razorback Ridge to corn. And Deadwood Underwood Planted the West side of Razorback Ridge to corn.

The corn did well, and all went well. For about four weeks—when the corn was ankle high. Then the boys decided to plow their respective corn fields.

At the crack of dawn, on a Monday morning, Oliver Tolliver set out to plow his cornfield on the East Side of Razorback Ridge. And at the same time, Deadwood Underwood set out to plow his cornfield on the West Side of Razorback Ridge.

As the golden sun was sinking in the West, the boys finished their respective tasks and each fed his mule and bedded him down for the night. Then each went home, had his supper, and turned in to sleep the innocent sleep of an honest man who has just followed a mule through thirty-eight miles of corn rows.

The next morning, Oliver Tolliver awoke and looked up his chimney at his cornfield. And, lo and behold, every single stalk had wilted and died.

And Deadwood Underwood awoke and looked up his chimney at his cornfield; and, lo and behold, every single stalk had wilted and died.

So, the boys got together and got an educated expert professor of agriculture from the University of Tennessee to come and see if he could figger out what had happened to their corn patches.

The educated expert Professor of Agriculture from the University of Tennessee took out his rule measure, and he measured Deadwood Underwood's Oliver Hillside Plow. Then he measured Oliver Tolliver's Oliver Hillside Plow.

Then he held up the ruler up to Razorback Ridge. The answer was obvious: Deadwood Underwood had plowed the roots off Oliver Tolliver's corn. And Oliver Tolliver had plowed the roots off Deadwood Underwood's corn.

But still, Silvertong Smith was silly enough to come back into the valley a-peddling his wares. Back within range of the guns of Oliver Tolliver and Deadwood Underwood.

The inscription, written on the plow handles at Smith's grave, reads: "Here lies Silly Silvertongue Smith. May the corn grow green on his grave, forevermore!"

—Joe Clark, hbss

GREAT GRANDPAPPY AND HIS GRAVITY BUGGY

Being a man of modest nature, I never talk about the many great achievements of my ancestors. Though I may have mentioned the time that my Great Grandpappy saved the colony from starvation. Or even the time that my Grandpappy taught his pigeons to fly upside down. But I'm certain that I never told you about the time my Great Grandpappy, on my Mother's side, invented his famous gravity controller.

This was the neatest little gadget you ever did see. About half the size of your hat. When Great Grandpappy clamped it onto the dashboard of his buggy—presto! ninety percent of the gravity became subject to the whims of Great Grandpappy's little gadget. That meant that his five-hundred-pound buggy now weighed an even fifty pounds.

With the gravitator, as Great Grandpappy called it, he could control the amount of gravity. And with what he called the AIMER, he could control the direction of the gravity pull. If, for instance, he pointed the Aimer straight up and turned on the gravity, his buggy would instantly fall straight up. Cut off the gravity while up in the air, and his buggy would simply float around in space. Point the Aimer down and turn on a bit of gravity, and his buggy would float gently to earth.

If he pointed the Aimer straight down the road and turned on the gravity, his buggy would fall straight down the road. If he turned on more or less gravity, the buggy would fall accordingly. By controlling the direction of the gravity pull, he could drive his buggy around in pretty much the same manner as we drive an automobile today. Except that there was no gas to buy. No repairs to make. No costly upkeep.

Since the buggy weighed only fifty pounds, there was no need for expensive rubber tires, shock absorbers, etc.

It wouldn't have been such a bad gadget even today.

Being powered by gravity, there was no such thing as skidding on curves or on icy roads. Nor was there any need for brakes, seat belts, or padded dashboards. To stop the buggy, you simply turned off or reversed the gravity and everybody and everything came to a safe, pleasant stop no matter the speed you were travelling.

Great Grandpappy even claimed that his gadget would eliminate the need to invent the automobile. This caused no end of arguments between Great Grandpappy and the neighbors.

Finally, the neighbors and the whole neighborhood became so involved that the whole community split into two factions: First there were the ones who maintained that Great Grandpappy's gadget would ruin the future of the country. They said there would be nothing for all the automobile workers to do when they migrated from Tennessee to Deetroit. But Great Grandpappy was a far-sighted man. He argued that people were going to invent a lot of labor-saving devices that they would have no time for jobs.

The second faction maintained that people would never be smart enough to invent the automobile and, therefore, Great Grandpappy was wasting his time because his Gravity Controller was designed to do away with a contraption that would never come into existence anyway. But the louder and longer they argued, the more convinced Great Grandpappy became. In fact, he began to have visions of making his Gravity Controller a hundred-percent perfect. This meant that his buggy would weigh absolutely nothing. It would float through the air. He began to maintain that once he got his gadget a hundred-percent efficient there wouldn't even be any need for the buggy. And that there would never be any need to invent the motor court, the motel, the expressway, the rest stop, the gas station, nor the hot dog stand.

According to Great Grandpappy, all you'd need to do, when he got his gadget perfected, was to clamp it onto your mantlepiece and presto (!), your whole house would become weightless. Then when you wanted to go anywhere you'd just set the Aimer, turn on the Gravity, and in a matter of a couple of hours, at the most, you could be settled down in your own home on the spot of your choosing anywhere on earth.

Up to this point, a good many of the neighbors were still listening but then Great Grandpappy had to up and go off the deep end. He up and predicted that his gadget would make it unnecessary to invent the airplane. To the neighbors, this was totally unthinkable. Why, to eliminate the invention of the airplane, they maintained, would mean that Orville and Wilbur Wright when they came along would have to go through life just making bicycles. And so they up and walked out on Great Grandpappy.

Now, the only person that Great Grandpappy had left to argue with was his Brother Annagus. And Uncle Annagus, though a patient man, was beginning to get a little fretted with Great Grandpappy.

Then one day Great Grandpappy was sitting on the front porch explaining for the thousandth time the merits of his Gravity Controller when he said, "By Jupiter, Annagus, this Gravity Controller will revolutionize . . . By Jupiter!" He suddenly exploded in high triumph. "I'll do it. I'll build a Jupiter Gravity Controller!" With that he left Uncle Annagus sitting on the porch and rushed downstairs to his basement workshop.

Great Grandma said afterwards that she could hear him down there all night long a-grinding and a-pounding and a-filing. And occasionally a-cussin a little. Then, one morning, just as she was building a fire in the stove to cook his breakfast, she heard him come a-charging up the stairs. Without so much as a good morning, he rushed out into the yard where the buggy was parked.

When she went out to call him in for breakfast he was busy fastening this strange little gadget onto the dashboard of the buggy. In fact, he was just putting in the very last screw. This done, he hopped into the buggy and set the Aimer straight for the Planet Jupiter. Then, before she could stop him, he pushed the button.

Whoosh!!! For just a few seconds, there was this thin pencil of blue smoke. Aiming straight for Jupiter. Then the breeze washed it away. And that was the last that anybody ever saw of Great Grandpappy.

For many years afterwards, Great Grandma would sit on the front porch on dark nights with her far-a-way specs on. She often claimed she could see a fire burning on Jupiter. "That," she would sigh, "is your Great Grandpa sitting by his campfire. And I'll betcha ten to one that he's cooking up some sort of devilment to get the neighbors in an uproar again."

At that time I didn't put much stock in Great Grandma's mutterings. But lately, I've been thinkin some about these here flyin saucers that folks have been seein in certain parts of the world. . . . It wouldn't sprize me one bit if there wasn't no flying saucers atall. . . . Just Great Grandpappy a flittin about in his old Gravity Buggy.

hbss

THE GHOST THAT WASN'T THERE

I'm only telling you this story because there are folks who are prone to argue long and loud about the pros and cons of ghosts. It happened when I was a wee lad back home in the hills of Tennessee.

It was one of those dark and stormy nights, the creek was up, the roads impassable, a mournful wind was soughing through the trees, and we had taken in a stranger to shelter from the storm. After this strange man with the deep-set eyes and tired, tired countenance had been fed and warmed, we all gathered around the fireside.

For a long, long time we sat silent in the firelight and watched the grotesque shadows cast by the dancing flames. Then the stranger cleared his throat, cast an apprehensive glance over his shoulder, hitched his chair a mite closer to the fire and, in a deep and distant voice began to talk:

"It was the darkest, meanest, nastiest most miserable night I ever did see. I had been over to see the Hollins girl down in Mournful Valley. Her Pa hadn't ever cottoned much to me, and on that night he had been consuming some of his own moonshine and was in a mood that was as foul as his makins.

"When I knocked at the door he set his dogs on me and then sent a hail of rifle balls zinging past me as I headed my horse down the mountain road lickety-split.

"My horse's hoofs drew sparks from the flinty road and my shirt tail fanned out behind me as the snarling bullets clipped off the pine boughs about my head. Nellie's Pa never was much of a shot.

"The cold drizzling rain had turned the red clay to grease underfoot as I crossed Piney Ridge and headed for Hungry Hollow. I sped on past Buzzard's Roost and swung my horse toward Desolate Nob. Since the road followed round the hillside, it was especially touchy at

this point; and I hadn't slowed as much as I should have.

"My thoughts were of Nellie—poor, dear, sweet girl, as me and my horse went sliding, tumbling and spinning down the slippery mountainside through the briar patch and sassafras thicket. Here she was a bare sweet-sixteen and about to become a widow before I ever had a chance to ask her Pa for her hand.

"My horse went over the precipice just ahead of me, and I heard him hit the bottom of the ravine just as I was saying 'Goodbye Sweet Nellie and Hello Saint Peter.' Then an Angel caught me up in his arms.

"Slowly, I opened my eyes and looked around for them Pearly Gates and them Golden Streets. There was nothing but darkness. Total darkness. I pinched myself and, believe it or not, I was still alive.

"It took a while for me to realize that I had landed in the top of a tall pine tree. Slowley, in the darkness, I slid down the pine tree. I'd gotten almost to the bottom when a limb broke and I fell into the creek.

"My horse was dead. I was going to have to make the trip across Ghost Mountain *on foot, through the rainy woods, on a dark night, past Old Settlers Graveyard, after, midnight.* Alone! My horse was the lucky one.

"I was the only living creature stirring on that dark and lonely night. And though Nellie loved me, Nellie's Pa certainly did not. My heart was filled with dread, and my veins were filled with ice as I trudged on through the eerie darkness.

"Occasionally, the moon shown through the tall trees as if trying to lend aid to a poor helpless traveler. But only for a second or two at a time. Each time it made an appearance, an ominous cloud would reach up and blot it out.

"On, on and on I trod. Through the eerie darkness. My heart growing heavier and heavier with each leaden step. I thought of Nellie and her Pa back in

Mournful Valley, of Ghost Mountain and Old Settlers Graveyard that hadn't been used for more than a hundred years. And of the awful fact that my path lay directly through that graveyard, on top of Ghost Mountain.

"I even thought of going back to face Nellie's Pa and his hot lead bullets, but an irresistible force drew me on towards Ghost Mountain. The only sound in the night was the falling rain and my pounding heart. The darkness laid a heavy hand over my straining eyes.

"I moved wearily up Ghost Mountain as in a daze. For a moment, as the moon peeked out, I saw a giant ghost reaching out for me. As I cried out in awful fright, I realized that it was only an old dead chestnut tree with its tall leafless branches reaching up like giant arms into the sky. Then a cloud, swirling in ghostly swiftness, blotted out the moon, leaving me to plod on in the darkness.

"I topped Ghost Mountain, and again the moon shown for a moment revealing the tombstones of Old Settlers Graveyard outlined against the baleful sky. Then again, darkness.

"Carefully, I threaded my way through the ancient tombstones. Then I came upon what seemed to be a small hill, a pile of fresh red earth. I attempted to move over it, but the rain had made it very slippery, and I went a sliding helter skelter until I was brought up with a thud. In the darkness I felt around me until I had felt four square corners. I had fallen into an open grave."

At this, all of us who were gathered around the fireside, shuddered a deep and fearful shudder. And at this very moment, a big gust of wind blew down the chimney and snuffed out the dying flames. Pappy quickly stirred up the embers and added some fresh wood. When the flames flared up again we looked about us but there was no stranger. Nor any sign of a stranger. Just an empty chair. Gently rocking back and forth in the eerie shadows of the firelight.

hbss

MEMORIES OF MY FIRST CHRISTMAS

Do you remember your first Christmas? Or did you, like most kids, sort of grow into it gradual like?

To me my first Christmas was sudden dramatic, warm and glorious. It was at Grandma's House.

It was Christmas Eve and my Aunts, Uncles and Cousins had come for the Holidays.

The kitchen was full of talk and laughter.

The livingroom was full of squeals and shouts.

The whole house reeked with the smell of gingerbread, molasses cookies, pumpkin pies and popping pop corn.

The fire danced ever so merrily in the huge fireplace.

Dried beans, dried apples, dried peppers and all manner of spices hung on slender threads, like so many strings of beads, from the heavy timbers that held up the livingroom ceiling.

The great log house that Grandpa had built before asking for Grandma's hand was alive and vibrating all over with the hustle and the bustle, the gay excitement, and the serene pleasure of loved ones who had not been together for a long, long time.

In the majestic woods that skirted the house, almost to the porches on two sides, the white, white snow was already most four inches deep and still falling profusely.

The boom of an occasional gunshot sent its echoes bounding and leaping across the hills and hollows as the men hunted squirrels, quail, and rabbits for tomorrow's feast. Christmas was coming to the Cumberlands for the first time. Or at least the first time in my memory.

Someone brought in a cedar tree from the woods outside and set it upright in a corner. The women covered it with strings of popcorn and then lit it with tiny red candles that Grandma had already made and waiting. It caused the livingroom to glow and the children to squeal with happiness. As darkness came on, the men swept the snow from huge logs with which they stoked the great fireplace. Then everyone to the diningroom. By the time supper was finished, the fire in the livingroom was going so well that the front door had to be left open to control the temperature.

After a brief rest the men took guns down from the overhead beams and walked out into the snow. We listened intently as the echoes from the first volley died away. Soon we heard it, the boom, and then the echoes came rolling down the valleys from Bob Day's high on the hill. Then there was Uncle Hugh's over on Towne Creek. And the Jim Underwoods over in the valley. And finally the Ike Mitchels down on Keg Branch. And in the faraway distance, through the gently falling snow, we could hear other guns open up and other echoes rolling up and down other hills and hollows.

As the echoes went laughing and leaping and dancing up and down the hills and hollows, up and down the mountains and valleys, they were bearing a message from neighbor to neighbor: WE ARE HAVING A MERRY CHRISTMAS AND HOPE THAT YOU ARE HAVING A MERRY CHRISTMAS, TOO.

We children played long and late that night with cousins we had never seen before. In fact, too late. Suddenly, amidst our shouts and laughter, the front door burst open and a shower of snow whipped across the livingroom. Frozen for a moment we stared in startled wonderment as Santa Claus, snow glistening on his red coat and long white whiskers, looked slowly around the room. Then, like a covey of frightened quail, we flew to hide under or behind whatever pieces of furniture we could find.

Peeking from our vantage points we heard Grandma telling Santa that if he would just stop by the Underwoods first she was sure that the children would be fast asleep by the time he got back. When the door closed behind Santa we all made one mad dash for bed.

As Grandpa was tucking my cousin Jeanie in, he asked "Are you sure that this will be enough kivers?" Jeanie looked up at Grandpa with her big blue eyes and asked, "Grandpa, you're getting awfully old arent you?" Grandpa was taken aback for a moment then he smiled gently and reckoned that he was getting pretty old. And Jeanie put her little arms around his neck and pulled him down and kissed him and said, "You meant covers when you said kivers, didn't you?"

For years afterward Grandpa always said he hoped that all of his grandchildren would get a lot of school education so that they could talk proper and be as sweet as Jeanie.

Christmas morning we kids were out of bed before Grandpa got the fire going good in the fireplace. And Santa had left each child one apple and one orange. Three brazil nuts and six peanuts, two sticks of peppermint candy and a suitable toy. My toy was a thingamajig with a long red handle like a popcorn popper. Only instead of a popcorn popper it had a pair of wheels on one end with a bell mounted between them. When you pushed this contraption along the floor, like pushing a vacuum cleaner, the bell went ding-ding, ding-ding.

Like the echoes the years go leaping and bounding by but the wonderment of Christmas still glows as warm and magical as ever.

hbss

THE FABLE OF THE BOY AND THE MULE

Said the mule as he pulled the plow one day
To the lad who guided it along the way.
"I'd give my life for a few bites of hay,
Why don't you unhitch me and run off and play?"
So the lad he up and unhitched the mule,
For the lad, as you can see, was quite a fool.
And the mule he let out an awful bray:
"What a fool of a lad," was all he could say.
And away he ran in search of some hay
And little was the plowing that got done that day.
The moral of this story as you may have guessed
Is that those who keep on plowing come out best.

—hbss

THE FABLE OF THE MAN AND THE ANT

A little black ant was hurrying across the sidewalk on its way to deliver some cookies to his sick aunt who lived in the park.

A man spied the little black ant hurrying across the sidewalk on its way to deliver some cookies to its sick aunt who lived in the park and felt it his duty to kill the little black aunt who was hurrying across the sidewalk to deliver some cookies to its sick aunt who lived in the park.

Just as he was about to lower his heavy boot on the little black ant who was hurrying across the sidewalk to deliver some cookies to its sick aunt who lived in the park, he thought "Why should I waste my energy crushing such an insignificant creature as a little black ant who is hurrying across the sidewalk to deliver some cookies to its sick aunt who lives in the park?" So he let him go.

Later on, as the man sat in the park reading his paper, the little black ant snook up side of his pant leg and bit him.

MORAL: Always do your duty, and you'll never get bit.

—hbss

THE WYOOTER HUNT

by Joe Clark, HBSS

I know full well that I shouldn't do this, but my son Junebug and some of his pals insist that I should tell you about Wyooter hunting.

Coon hunting, as I pointed out before, is a fine mild sport for folks who like to spend a pleasant evening without too much wear and tear on the seat of the pants.

Wyooter hunting now, that's something else. I shall never forget the last time me and my three brothers went on a Wyooter hunt. It was one of those dank, dark, cold nights with a bit of a mist and just enough cold rain to chill your bones to the marrow. A night when the stock huddles close to the barn, the chickens roost high in the trees, the dogs hide under the woodshed and the water oozels insists on coming into the house to sleep in the wood box behind the kitchen stove.

So me and my three brothers set out with our famous dog Old Trouble. We called him Old Trouble because any varmint, from coon to grizzley, that crossed his path was in for a mess of trouble. Old Trouble had a reputation as the strongest, toughest, fastest, fiercest, fightenist, dog that ever came down the pike. And besides that he was especially good on Wyooters.

First, we set off across Ghost Mountain. They call it Ghost Mountain because there is an ancient graveyard right on the very top of it. And many's the time and tale of hunters who have been chased off of it by the ancient ghosts that rise from this old graveyard. But I don't have time to go into detail about any of these at the moment.

We crossed the mountain taking the trouble to skirt the graveyard by only about a quarter of a mile because we knew that there would be no ghosts out tonight. Nothing alive or dead, human, varmint, or ghost dares to come out when Wyooters are on the prowl. And we knew by the shiver in our bones that Wyooters were on the prowl this night.

We angled down the backside of Ghost Mountain into Lonesome Valley. And then all the way down the valley and up Snake Hollow. At the head of Snake Hollow we came upon three giant oak trees that had been freshly pulled up by the roots. Old Trouble sniffed these, bristled, and then growled a low rumbling growl. So we knew that we were hot on the trail of a real live Wyooter.

Pretty soon Old Trouble took off the side of Clinch Mountain, still rumbling. And with us all hot on his tail. We didn't want to tangle with no Wyooter without Old Trouble around. We topped the mountain at full speed and looked down into the valley on the other side. Even if I could, I wouldn't dare describe the terrible scene that we saw below us in that valley, because it might frighten you right out your wits. Might even scare you to death. Every tree and every shrub throughout the whole length and breadth of the valley had been pulled up by the roots and turned upside down. And every house and every barn and every outbuilding looked as if some giant hand had picked it up and then smashed it against the ground like a Humpty Dumpty never to be put together again. And bones! Everywhere bones, bones, bones! Nothing but bones.

Old Trouble froze in his tracks. My three brothers froze in their tracks. And even I hesitated for a moment.

Pretty soon Old Trouble saw his duty. And when Old Trouble saw his duty, he did his duty. He was that kind of a dog. He took out after that Wyooter and he chased it up a persimmon tree. And he went right up that tree after it. And he brought it down by the nap of the neck. And he shook it and shook it until it cried like a baby.

And then he gently wiped away its tears and sent it home to its mamma. Old Trouble always was a compassionate sort of a dog.

And, from that day till this, Wyooters have been fairly civil critters. A few have even been known to make reasonably good pets.

Hardly ever do they eat men anymore. Or even little boys.

Joe Clark, hbss

WHITE LIGHTNIN'

Through the trees among the waving laurel bushes, I saw them. Their guns at the ready. Their sinister faces set. Their beady eyes darting this way and that. They must have parked their car over somewhere around Gobbler's Nob and then made their way on foot up the narrow and treacherous Snake Hollow.

But a body doesn't spend a lifetime manufacturing the holy water without learning a little something. So we were ready for 'em. I touched Glenn's arm to warn him, but he had already seen them coming up the path in the hollow directly below us only about fifty feet away. The taller one was in the lead.

Our little "coffee mill" was located back of an old rail fence in a small cave in a laurel thicket on the side of Hog Ridge about fifty feet above the narrow overgrown path that wound up the hollow between Hog Ridge and Razorback Ridge on its way up Hoot Own Mountain. The revvies were sneaking up this little path in the narrow hollow just below us. Just over Razorback Ridge, above and beyond the revvies, we had our first stick of dynamite planted.

Out of the corner of my eye I could see Glenn's hand reaching for that tiny black sewing thread that led to it. Suddenly, whoom!!! The whole ridge seemed to tremble as the dynamite exploded and the echoes went rolling up and down the hollows.

The revvies nearly jumped out of their skins and we almost busted trying to keep from roaring with laughter as they started clawing up the steep side of Razorback Ridge to see what had happened to the other side.

This would keep 'em busy for a few minutes till we could seal off the cave and get our rifles. Then Glenn headed up Dead Man's Peak and I shinnied up Lover's Rock to wait for our revvies to return. We'd barely got settled in when they came sneaking back over the ridge and down into the hollow again. I waited till they came into a little clearing, and then I pulled a second string that set off a stick of dynamite directly back of them. When they wheeled around with their backs to us, I drew a quick bead and pulled the trigger. That sent the tall one's hat sailing off into the underbrush. Almost simultaneously Glenn's gun boomed from Dead Man's Peak, and the short one's hat flew up and landed in a cluster of laurel blooms.

I guess them fellers must have thought somebody had declared war on 'em because one uvem yelled, "Let's get out of here!" and they took off down the hollow like a couple of scared hants.

We knew that it would take them a good half hour to get to their car at Gobbler's Nob and get down to Dal Gulley's Store where they would probably call for reinforcements.

They always called for reinforcements. And then went back and tramped down a lot of laurel bushes, but it never got 'em nowhere.

By headin' down the back side of Hoot Own Mountain we could easily make it to Dal's in twenty minutes. Sure enough in about six minutes they come sidling in lookin' sort of sheepish like. I was leanin' casually against the counter having some conversation with Dal and Glenn was seated on a nail keg whittlin' and carryin' on with old man Whit Coleman about weather and crops and things.

Old Whit looked up at the two revvies, eyed them sharply for a few seconds and then asked, "Didn't I see you fellers go by here headed towards Gobbler's Nob in an old Chevy two or three hours ago?" The revvies admitted that he may have.

"Well, I declare," Uncle Whit declared, "my old eyes must be gittin' a lot worse'n I thought. I could a swore that both of you fellers was a wearin' hats when you went by."

—hbss

It is sad but true
My friend
This little visit
Here must end.
hbss